The Marvel of Biographical Bookkeeping

Francis Nenik

Translated from the German by Katy Derbyshire

For Ivan Blatný and Nicholas Moore,
who took new liberties after being robbed of their own.

When the critic George Steiner looked through the entries for the *Sunday Times* Baudelaire translation competition he was judging in 1968, he was no doubt a little surprised. Someone had submitted more than thirty versions of the same poem.

That someone was Nicholas Moore, an aspiring English poet during the 1940s, who had somehow disappeared from the radar at the end of that decade and had not made a reappearance since.

That is, Nicholas Moore had never really disappeared; instead he had slipped unnoticed into the workings of time and, in addition, had suffered a series of blows of fate, all of which he had somehow survived. Yet in the world of letters, Nicholas Moore was a dead man, catapulted out of a literary machinery revolving ever faster, and often merely around itself.

1948 was his fateful year. And it went like this:

Nicholas Moore, a twenty-nine-year-old author of numerous poetry collections, editor of diverse magazines and anthologies and the recipient of respected literary prizes – Nicholas Moore, a frequent and welcome guest in the paper worlds of

*W*hen the journalist Jürgen Serke came across a slim man with a small cut on his freshly shaven cheek in St. Clements Hospital in Ipswich in 1981, he was no doubt a little surprised. The man had been declared dead more than thirty years previously.

That man was Ivan Blatný, an aspiring Czech poet during the 1940s, who had absconded from his delegation on a trip to London in 1948, stayed in London and then disappeared.

That is, Ivan Blatný had never really disappeared; instead he was struggling with paranoia as a result of his escape and exile, which took him behind the secure walls of various English hospitals. Yet in the world of letters, Ivan Blatný was a dead man, his name erased by a literary machinery surviving on suppression and silencing.

1948 was his fateful year. And it went like this:

Ivan Blatný, a twenty-eight-year-old author of numerous poetry collections, prose works and children's books, recently adopted into the official canon of Czech literary history – Ivan Blatný, an author awarded a grant and dispatched to London by the national writers' syndicate –

3

Anglo-American poetry, leading an almost secure life in comparison to other poets – Nicholas Moore, who dedicated a large part of his poetry to his wife Priscilla and even named a book after her – Nicholas Moore is abandoned: by his wife, by financial independence, and by the good fortune of being printed and read.

The only person, it seems, to take an interest in Nicholas Moore thenceforth is the man who steals his wallet in the crush at London's Petticoat Lane market: containing not so much money as letters of inestimable value – letters that Moore had exchanged over the years with the American poet Wallace Stevens and the British writer Osbert Sitwell.

All that remains is lonely, wasted land. Everywhere around him. Not only has Priscilla left, but she has also taken their daughter with her, and Moore has to give up the flat where the three of them previously lived. He finds a new place to live (where he stays for the rest of his life): a small ground-floor flat in a desolate part of southeast London.

Ivan Blatný, who was a member of the influential artists' group Skupina 42 and schooled his poetic manifesto within the collective – Ivan Blatný abandons everything: his home, his friends, his position in Czech literary history.

The only person, it seems, to take an interest in Ivan Blatný thenceforth is an agent from the Czechoslovakian secret service, whom someone has charged with tempting the poet back for propaganda purposes. A hopeless undertaking. Blatný, the spy reports, has come to terms with his new life in hospital and lost all contact to the outside world.

All that remains is dead, unfamiliar land. Everywhere around him. Not only has Blatný gone into exile, but he has also found no new home here and soon, mentally defeated, has to surrender his new-found freedom again. He finds a new place to live (where he stays for the rest of his life): a series of psychiatric hospitals, the first of which – Claybury – is in the northeast of London.

Nor do things look any better from a financial perspective. Money, the lack of which grants writing full authenticity in the mind of many a critic but leaves nothing more than a hole in the writer's stomach, is now more than just tight; the time of parental subsidies is over and Moore's income from his poetic undertakings is so small that he is forced to exchange writing poetry for gardening and take on a job with a London seed merchant.

By the time Moore's poetry volume *Recollections of the Gala* is published in 1950, interest is minor and the critique is devastating. Nicholas Moore, the journals write, is a jaded man after an insipid entertainment, his poems a lukewarm rehash of a time so very tepid by now. Shortly after that, Nicholas Moore disappears from the literary world.

In the workings of time, the bodies twitch – and the critics alongside it merely shrug their shoulders.

The twentieth century has meanwhile reached half-time. The war is over, the new era is manifest – and Moore's work and the New Apocalyptics movement with which it has been associated are now nothing but objects of better judgement, subjected

Nor do things look any better from a literary perspective. The road from genius to insanity, which onlookers often consider to be predetermined in a writer's innermost workings, is for Ivan Blatný one determined by distant, unfamiliar powers. And even if that's not the case and for him, having suffered from anxiety during the war, the road from lyricist to lunatic is only a fork in the path inside his skull, London is still a thousand miles away from Brno.

A few of Blatný's former fellow travellers, meanwhile, send verses to England and call him a degenerate poet who will one day pay for his betrayal of the Czech people. Ivan Blatný, the journals write, has been lost to Czech literature since the moment he decided to stay on foreign soil. Shortly after that, Czech radio declares him dead.

In Prague, they hang one of Blatný's fellow poets – while the writers all around him exclaim, 'What a pity.'

The twentieth century has meanwhile reached half-time. The war is over, the new era is manifest – and Blatný's work and Skupina 42, which has been rejected for its avant-garde borrowings, are now nothing but objects of an overcome ideology, subjected to accusations and to ridicule, erasure and oblivion. In a word: history. Nicholas Moore's apocalypse, however, has only just begun.

It is 1951, and Moore, only recently considered one of the most hopeful English poets, who made the writing of the American Henry Miller known in the kingdom of the Puritans through his work with *Poetry London*, makes a living by constructing rock gardens in the arid suburbs of a land once covered in forests. And yet there is one last straw for him to cling to, for he, Nicholas Moore, the poet, has been appointed co-editor of *Poetry London*. Along with others, he had taken over the financially ailing magazine in 1949 from a Tamil mover and shaker who ran all manner of poetic rags in London and claimed to originate from a family of Ceylon royalty. However, the switch of editors has taken place too late, the magazine is hopelessly behind its former sales figures of 10,000 copies – and the print run falls and falls. Nicholas Moore's last literary rising founders in a subscriber apocalypse. There is no longer any place for him in poetically refurbished Britain.

In America, meanwhile, his former fellow-traveller, the poet, critic, mover and shaker *humiliations, charges and trials. In a word: history. Ivan Blatný's struggle for his own existence, however, has only just begun.*

It is 1954, and Blatný, only recently considered one of the most hopeful Czech poets, who made it onto the pages of the New York Times *with his escape from the 1948 writers' delegation selected by the communist powers-that-be in Prague, makes a living writing short pieces for the BBC and Radio Free Europe. And yet there is one last straw for him to cling to, for he, Ivan Blatný, the poet, has been granted asylum in England. Ground down by his fear of a communist abduction, he had already checked himself into psychiatric hospital in 1948 but left soon afterwards, continuing to write his radio pieces and a few poems on the side while holding lectures on the situation in his home country. However, the switch between worlds does not work well for long. In 1954 the doctors diagnose Ivan Blatný with paranoid schizophrenia. Fear has won out; the asylum is now final. The gates close. Ivan Blatný's escape ends in the smallest possible space. Claybury Psychiatric Hospital is now his new home.*

In Czechoslovakia, meanwhile, his former fellow-traveller, the poet, prose and stage writer Vítězslav Nezval,

Thurairajah Tambimuttu, has exchanged *Poetry London* for *Poetry New York*, bringing him the goodwill of the New York arts scene in general and of a lady by the name of Winthrop Bushnell Palmer in particular. Nicholas Moore, however, stays in his small London ground-floor flat, takes the train to work across the city every day and in his free time starts cultivating irises. The apocalypse, it appears, has switched to stand-by.

And yet, as hard as Nicholas Moore tries, he writes fewer poems with every year. Having once been known for his sheer inexhaustible output of poetry, he hardly puts anything down on paper during the 1950s. And finally the apocalypse returns to his life, butting in like an unwanted guest who had simply gone for a quick pee between revelations.

But God, who's nothing but a dog backwards, taught him to carry on.

Moore marries for a second time, a woman from London's suburban middle-class, and fathers a son and a daughter. But the daughter dies at an early age and his wife is in poor mental health. She can soon no longer take care of the boy, who is put into an orphanage. Nicholas Moore himself is has exchanged poetic surrealism for socialist realism, bringing him the goodwill of Prague's communists in general and the status of a national artist in particular. Ivan Blatný, however, stays in Claybury, walks around the hospital's grounds every day and in his free time reads all the magazines people give him. He has crossed two borders. He is an exile in exile. The struggle for his own existence, it appears, can only be continued in sheltered spaces.

And yet, as hard as Ivan Blatný tries, he writes fewer poems with every year. Having exchanged rhyming letters with his father as a child and translated Goethe's Sorcerer's Apprentice into Czech at the age of eleven, he hardly puts anything down on paper during the 1950s. And the little he does write gets thrown away. By the attendants, who think Blatný is a lunatic who thinks he's a writer.

But God the linguist taught him to breathe.

After nine years in Claybury, Ivan Blatný is transferred to House of Hope in Ipswich, meaning town with a port, where Ivan Blatný is now stranded. He stays aground there for fourteen years, only once receiving visitors. Jan Smarda, his cousin, comes to see him secretly. In his wake he has a teacher by the name of Barina, an overworked, falls sick, contracts diabetes, can barely keep the household running. The small flat falls into neglect from the outside in. Local youths throw stones at the grime-stiffened windows. It doesn't appear as if the apocalypse were going to elapse.

A few years later, diabetes has confined Nicholas Moore to a wheelchair. One of his legs has to be amputated due to gangrene at the end of the 1960s. A disability pension keeps him above water. He does not give up gardening, however. He wheels himself outside between the remnants of a discarded existence, straight to the place where his home-cultivated irises grow. Where a Japanese cherry tree stands. And where rocks of limestone lie. Nicholas Moore wheels himself into his garden, leans over, tipping his wheelchair at a 45-degree angle, digs a hole in the ground and plants bulbs in it. The apocalypse has drawn the short straw.

Nicholas Moore writes again, starting over from the beginning in the 1960s. Nicholas Moore writes. And writes. And does not get into print.

admirer of Blatný. Blatný himself starts writing more towards the end of the 1960s. But the attendants still throw everything away. It appears as if the struggle for his own existence cannot even be won in sheltered spaces.

A few years later, Ivan Blatný is taken four miles further west, to Ipswich's St. Clements Hospital, a tangle of red bricks from England's glory days. He moves into a room with nine other men on Bixley Ward. From now on he spends his time running errands and polishing endless floors. In between, however, he waits for his judgement from the ostrakismos. He still does not give up writing, nevertheless. He simply carries on. One day a woman approaches him, takes his papers and goes away with them. From then on she comes to him once a week, takes the paper he has written on, collects it and secures it in metal containers. In the struggle for his own existence, chance has played a trick on fate.

Ivan Blatný has stopped writing for the rubbish bin, starting over from the beginning in the 1970s. Ivan Blatný writes. And writes. And gets into print. In Canada.

Whatever Nicholas Moore sends out comes back by return of post, rejected by the people who sit at the gear-switches with their degrees in literature, producing firings, sorting out rubbish. It's all just a question of names, affirmations and categories. Nicholas Moore, however, disappears as a gap in English literary history. Only in one 1963 anthology are a few of his poems published.

And yet Nicholas Moore goes on writing, writing more and more, hammering his fingers sore on his old typewriter, living and writing day in, day out in the midst of mountains of paper, which never stop growing and spreading, as if he wanted to annex England to the Alps.

But it's not the wide world of transatlantic poetry, it's a small ground-floor flat in a desolate part of southeast London where a poet manoeuvres his wheelchair around paper mountains – and nothing ever gets out.

A small king of a realm of rains, he is trapped on an island made of paper, which he attempts to seal against the rising damp with every sheet he writes upon. And around him the things the sea of domestic life has washed up in the form of habits over the years: wine bottles, newspapers, cigar boxes,

At home, however, Ivan Blatný's work is still banned. After the end of the Prague Spring a reissue of his poems is thrown in the pulping machine by the people who hit harder with words than any poet. It's all just a question of names, affirmations and categories. Ivan Blatný, however, disappears as a gap in Czech literary history. Only in one 1963 anthology are a few of his poems published.

And yet Ivan Blatný goes on writing, writing more and more, hammering his fingers sore on his old typewriter, which may not have Czech accents above the English letters but does produce a replica of the Bohemian-Moravian mountain range out of paper.

But it's not Brno, it's a desk in a corner of the workshop in a mental hospital in Ipswich, England where a poet sits among madmen who still steal the chocolate out of his bedside cabinet.

A poet in jester's shoes, he is trapped in his double exile, which grants him, turned inwards, a memory of days past. Of Marqui, the kitten, which must be old and tired by now. Of Lhoták, the painter, whose pictures he loves. Of the goat battling with a garland of potato leaves in the village graveyard. Of the motorcycle with a green sidecar.

magazines, garden tools, books, jazz records, biscuit tins, cricket bats, chocolate – breakwaters against the silence and the revelations of ignorance.

And so he continues, sending out into the world whatever he can. He, the king of a small English realm, translates Baudelaire's "Spleen" precisely thirty-one times – and submits his series piece by piece. To the *Sunday Times* in London, attn George Steiner, Baudelaire Translation Competition. The sender of the rewritings is Nicholas Moore, 89 Oakdene Road, St Mary Cray, Kent. Also Lhoso Cinaremo, who has the same address. But Helga Nevvadotoomuch takes part too, as do Phil Okes-Box-Wunnayay, Lester Younggold, Rosine MaCoolh, Papa Nicolas, Kenelme Sexnoth Pope, Jago McFaithfull Fabb of the MacBeth's Firefighters and H R Fixon-Boumphrey, allegedly President-elect of the Society for Multiple Injuries.

At the end of the competition a certain Angus MacPhee wins, not one of the names on Nicholas Moore's list of pseudonyms. But that's not the end of the world, not an apocalypse, not even literary pain.

And of his grandmother, sitting in the inn with him. Memory is his future path, and he guards over it.

And so he continues, writing the fiction of his own story. He, the king of a small Czech realm in English lands, composes poems day after day and submits them in half a dozen languages. To Sixty-Eight Publishers in Toronto, attn Josef Škvorecký, re: Bixley Remedial School. *The sender of the writings is Frances Meacham, a retired English nurse who had once fallen in love with a Czech pilot, decades ago during the war. Their relationship has long since failed and Miss Meacham is just as lonely as Mr Blatný. But she has a friend in Brno. She had visited him two years previously, in 1977. And there she happened to meet the teacher Barina, who had visited the poet Blatný in England eight years before that.*

At the end of the trip Miss Meacham goes to see Mr Blatný, takes his sheets of paper and takes care of them. In sheltered spaces, fate sometimes turns out to be not such a one-way street after all.

And Moore? He sits there and enjoys what he sees: thirty-one versions of a single poem, the proof of the untranslatability of poetry turned sheer on its head, thirty-one versions that are neither originals nor forgeries and not even both, which does not trouble their creator to any great extent, however, for some time before he wrote a sonnet about translating and scattered a few lines into it of something that must originally have been an excellent Czech poem, but in translation was merely a chain of words made comprehensible, with no other raison d'être.

Moore's thirty-one Baudelaire versions are published in 1973. It is the last volume of his poetry to appear during his lifetime.

Nicholas Moore is now fifty-five years old. He celebrates with wine, a satirical poem and French chocolate biscuits. He has diabetes. The gangrene is nudging at his remaining foot. It runs up and down his leg. It can hardly wait. But Nicholas Moore has already died. The gangrene has no idea of the comings and goings of literature. Though all it need do is to ask the rust on the workings of time – that eats its way through just as fast. Nicholas Moore, however, is celebrating his birthday. He

And Blatný? He sits there and meanders, writing, through space, time and languages, is happy and writes, as it were, very angry a new poem, he doesn't know where the arteries are, he doesn't see the human body, he is the most inferior man on earth, the bad weather is going on, and he cannot explain his poetry, it is comprehensible like a calendar, and that's why he'll have a cigarette now, even though he'd like to explain his poetry he doesn't know how it is, ovošče, je n'ai pas d'espace, you can't explain his work, it's a nevertheless-language that spills across the paper, whether togetanashtray or not.

Blatný's collected works written in the hospital are published in 1979. It is the first volume of his poetry for over thirty years.

Ivan Blatný is now sixty years old. He celebrates by climbing into the chalice of a flower and disappearing. His congratulators see nothing but his thin body sliding through the interior of the stem. Things are taking a downward turn, one might think. But Ivan Blatný merely slips a little further down. Then he stops, cuts a hole in the scape and looks out of the window. He clutches a shard in his hand, his name written on it. For the ostrakismos. His congratulators see the sap flowing out of the flower. Ivan Blatný, however, is celebrating his birthday. He is now sixty is now fifty-five years old. Only one of his poems has been translated into German to date. That was almost thirty years ago. Nicholas Moore was famous at the time. He wrote poems. One of them begins with the words: "Do I make my disasters clear?"

Until that time, that is, until the apocalypse reveals itself as a form of full stop, Nicholas Moore goes on writing. A total of three thousand poems. Only a fraction of them are saved. By one man who is interested in him.

He's not a thief but a writer. His name is Peter Riley, and when he walked into Nicholas Moore's flat in 1984, the purity of the art in the midst of all the junk and dirt, the sicknesses and the decay must have seemed like a bad joke to him. In the sea of domestic substance, the old man's habits had crusted over with coal dust and food detritus, the breakwaters solidified into rubbish tips. There he sat, the once and former ruler of a kingdom, a diabetic and confined to his wheelchair, in a squalid maisonette in a desolate London suburb, the one-legged product of a soundless vanishing, catapulted out of literary life in torturous slow motion.

Did I make his disasters clear?

years old. Only one of his poems has been translated into German to date. That was almost thirty years ago. Ivan Blatný was famous at the time. He wrote poems. But now he says: "I am locked and gone."

Until that time, that is, until the gates open before the dead body, Ivan Blatný goes on writing. Hundreds, perhaps thousands of poems. Only a fraction of them are saved. By three men who are interested in him.

They're not spies but writers. Their names are Vratislav Färber, Zbyněk Hejda and Antonín Petruželka, and when they published a samizdat edition of Bixley Remedial School *in 1982, Blatný's old-style surrealist poetry must have seemed like an ironic joke at the cost of Czech socialism. In his double exile, the poet in the jester's shoes had gained an insight into days long gone. Those who Ivan Blatný once left behind have lived on in England, and they now come crawling out in Prague. Marqui the kitten, the goat in the village graveyard, Lhoták the painter, the grandmother at the inn, even a green motorcycle with a sidecar rise up from the depths. Ivan Blatný, however, is in hospital in England.*

Can you see him, locked and gone?

Or is there more than this? Other things, perhaps even happiness?

Are there not poems between all the dirt, the filth and all the vanishing? Buried in flowerpots, wedged between the dirty crockery in the sink, lying on the floor, crinkled, crumpled and decorated with chocolate stains?

Nicholas Moore has made himself comfortable on his island, in his realm of paper. He knows he won't drown. The island is watertight; it won't sink now. He has built it up over the years like a coral reef. The poems on the sheets at the top resting on a swamp of themselves. He has constructed his isle atop his own grave. There are even flowers. And French biscuits. And wine.

· Epilogue: 26 January 1986

A few hours before the end of this life's apocalypse reveals itself to the poet Nicholas Moore and he realizes that God, seen backwards, was often enough a dog, he is lying in a hospital bed and writing a poem.

Or is there more than this? Other things, perhaps even happiness?

Does Ivan Blatný not go on writing? Does he not fill pad after pad with his poems? And once the Iron Curtain has fallen and possesses only the scrap value of a bad memory, don't friends from the old homeland visit him again at last?

Ivan Blatný has made himself comfortable in the sheltered space of his exile. He knows he won't leave England now. He doesn't need to either. They're all back with him again. And those who don't come, can't come, no longer exist, he writes to his side. He has prepared poems for them. They'll talk about literature for days. The world will be full of life again.

Epilogue: 5 August 1990

A few hours before the poet Ivan Blatný hears the final bell in the fight for his own existence and notices that God the linguist can also sound in Czech, he is lying in a hospital bed and writing a poem.

Ivan Blatný/Nicholas Moore
—
A Correspondence

Author's Note

It was originally my intention to include a short prose piece about Ivan Blatný at this point. In the course of my research, however, in February 2011, I came across previously unknown material in the London Metropolitan Archives, to be precise an exchange of letters between Blatný and Nicholas Moore dating from 1962/63. As these documents have not been published to date and both poets are now widely forgotten or almost unknown, I would like to take this opportunity to reproduce the letters in full.

This printing of the letters is preceded by some details on the circumstances under which they were found and a few general comments on the letters themselves. I have also included a brief glossary of names, intended to aid comprehension and classification of the persons mentioned in the letters.

On the circumstances of finding the letters

All the letters published here were contained in an archive file labelled Bl-1/1425, part of a collection of files dealing with the London County Council Public Health Department and listed in the London Metropolitan Archives under the reference code LCC/PH/MENT. This collection consists of a large number of documents on the subject of mental illness and mental disability. It includes, ia, minutes of meetings of asylum officers at various London County Council-run psychiatric care institutions, general reports on the subject of mental illness and minutes of the Executive Committee of the London Association for the Care of the Mentally Defective. Additionally, the collection contains studies on venereal disease in relation to mental disability, newspaper cuttings relevant to the work of the Asylums Committee, lists of patients, reports by asylum wardens and samples of case cards and papers of both children and adults with mental disabilities. Letters or other personal documents, in contrast, other than those published here, were not to be found anywhere else in the collection, which occupies 5.18 linear metres of shelf space. There is thus some indication that the letters have found their way into the collection mistakenly – an assumption supported by the fact that, according to the archive's internal categorisation, the material listed under the above reference code covers the period from 1938–1960 only. Though Blatný had been admitted to Claybury Hospital as a long-term patient in 1954, the letters in question date to the years 1962/63. Nor were there any other items relating to Ivan Blatný's stay at Claybury Hospital in the other documents on the institution in the London Metropolitan Archives. Documents on his transfer to the Ipswich 'House of Hope' in 1963 have not yet been located either.

On the letters

The fact that not only the letters from Nicholas Moore to Ivan Blatný, but also those from Blatný to Moore have been preserved, is due to the fortuitous circumstance that Blatný made copies of his letters in a notebook contained in the file. The possibility that these copies might be mere drafts appears unlikely, since the transcriptions contain no crossings-out, etc. Whether such drafts existed or Blatný committed his letters directly to paper cannot be determined with any certainty. No such drafts have been found to date. Nevertheless, the letter of 16 March 1963 shows that, at least in this particular case, Blatný wrote in several stages.

Equally, there is no doubt that the letters transcribed to the notebook were not only written but also posted, as Nicholas Moore refers to Blatný's comments throughout the correspondence.

Without exception, Ivan Blatný's letters published here reproduce the version contained in the notebook. The extent to which they correspond with the posted letters can only be established by comparison with any letters possibly present among Nicholas Moore's posthumous papers. Sadly, the author has not yet had the opportunity to view the latter. What can, however, be said, is that Blatný – apparently in view of his addressee's native language – composed his letters solely in English and did not, as in a number of his poems, put his thoughts onto paper in Czech, German or French, whereby the language in the poems occasionally switches mid-paragraph or mid-stanza and Blatný alternates from one language to the next. There is no indication of this in his letters to Moore, however, although other entries in the notebook do contain traces of Blatný's linguistic microcosm.

Lingual proficiency notwithstanding and alongside all of their other peculiarities, the letters from both Ivan Blatný and Nicholas Moore do contain occasional minor orthographic flaws. Obvious mistakes have therefore been tacitly corrected, while idiosyncratic spellings and punctuation have been retained.

To conclude, a few words on the notebook itself. It consists of 164 unpaginated sheets, its exterior plain black and its interior covered from the first page to the last with Blatný's large handwriting, which allows only few words to each line. Alongside the letters, it contains mainly minor everyday observations, some of them tending towards the poetic, whereby real poems remain an exception. (Insofar as such a distinction may be made in Blatný's case.) Additionally, there are a number of quotes from various writers and – particularly in the first pages and at the end of the book – reflections on Claybury Hospital, where Blatný lived at that point. The period covered by dates provided in the notes extends from 6 December 1962 (page 2) to 15 May 1963 (page 159).

With regard to Nicholas Moore's letters, these were all found inside the back cover of the notebook and had all – apart from one – been returned to their envelopes. The exception is Moore's letter dated 26 April 1963, which the author wrote to Blatný in the wake of his visit to a number of Oxford libraries, not using normal letter paper, however, but the unprinted reverse side of an information leaflet from the Taylorian Library, folded up, its edges glued together and then sent to Blatný in this letter-like form. For Moore, who wrote dozens, if not hundreds of such letters, which he referred to as 'pomenvylopes' and equipped with quotes, poems, satirical verses or other texts, such a procedure was common. For Blatný, in contrast, it is likely to have been a highly unusual occurrence to have received a letter that contained on its outside not only his name and address, but also the entire borrowing rules of an Oxford library.

Ivan Blatný to Nicholas Moore

Claybury Hospital
Woodford Bridge, Essex

10th December 1962

My dear sir,
Please excuse this letter. You do not know me and I
know nothing about you. We have never met. Yet I
have been told we had led similar lives. I don't
know whether that is the case. I don't even know
whether such a thing is possible. But Britain is
great. And why not write a missive from a clayey
grave and imagine it blowing across the rolled-out
land? Doctor Martin has promised me a magazine if
I write to you. I assume he will read this letter
before you receive it. So I shall stop here.

Ivan Blatný

Nicholas Moore to Ivan Blatný

89 Oakdene Road,
St Mary Cray, Kent

14th December 1962

Esteemed Mr Blatný,

I know neither you nor Mr Martin, and I'm sure he had his reasons if he promised you a magazine. For my part, I have no opinion on the matter.

With regard to your person, however, I can merely speculate. You live in Claybury Hospital, or work there. From the small extract from the *Times*, which propelled itself over the edge of the table as I opened your letter, I gather that you held a lecture on the case of Czechoslovakia at the 'Allied Circle' in London on 12th May 1948. (According to the weather forecast printed above the announcement of your lecture, it must have been a day of a veritably archetypical English nature. Fog at first, dispersing during the morning, coupled with variable winds, mainly from the North, possibly thunderstorms in the afternoon and later rain.) Be that as it may, let's not talk about the weather. Your letter contained a poem written by me, and the impression arises that you (or Mr Martin) believe me to be a poet. Well, I'm afraid I must disappoint you, for I am not one. That is to say, not any longer. And if I am after all, then only in my own way.

So should you have sent me the poem, Mr Blatný, I apologise. Should it have been Mr Martin, however, who cut it out of the *Times Literary Supplement* and enclosed it with your letter post hoc, do please pass on my best wishes – if he is not doing so himself at this very moment – and say that Nicholas Moore is standing before the grave of his poetic ego and laughing like a lunatic. I assume it was that line which prompted a doctor in a psychiatric institution to arrange such a thing. Logic has a firm standing in my mind, however, and my will follows suit. My cranial interior is not insane.

Yours sincerely,
Nicholas Moore

Nicholas Moore to Ivan Blatný

89 Oakdene Road,
St Mary Cray, Kent

30th December 1962

Mr Blatný, I don't know whether you have already received my letter and whether you will write to me again or not, but I have just found out that a poet whose name probably means as little to you as yours does to me has recently passed away. His name was Vincent Swart – and I shall tell you about him. (Please don't misunderstand me; my words to you are not a replication, but a groundlessness with a hint of coincidence, which I propose to indulge. All I hope from it is to find a reader in you. And perhaps two, if we include Mr Martin.)

Vincent Swart died on the 15th of December, and it is unlikely that he took any notice of it himself. He was fifty-one, sick, impoverished and, I fear, intoxicated. As far as I recall, his feet were two great lumps of flesh, yet his mind was so bright that his tongue remained sharp for the length of his life, no matter how many Gordian knots the alcohol tied in it.

To avoid creating a false impression, I had no particular relationship to him, and God alone knows what he had been up to over the past few years. He was an erratic fellow, and the only thing I can say with certainty is that he placed his spirit in the life-long service of the revolutionary cause and bred chickens unsuccessfully on the side. (Probably as unsuccessfully as I breed flowers.) Swart was a South African anarchist and an English poet in one person. One who had to leave England in 1940 because he belonged in a non-beleaguered country, according to his papers. His own land had long since been occupied, but that the siege was an inner one. I don't know if that was what killed him. But I do know that Swart had a refuge inside himself, an air-raid shelter made of paper, though its walls were at least as soaked in alcohol as they were in ink.

I had published one of his poems in *Seven* in 1940, and later, I believe it was 1945, Douglas Newton and I did so with another of his pieces. After that I lost track of him, although Swart is supposed to have returned to London again in the early 50s and lived there for a few years. By that point, however, I was boarding in Kent and living on my memories, and the only other thing I know about him (from where, I cannot say, but I did know it before I read his eight-line obituary in the newspaper) is that he was part of a group of artists in the South Africa of the 30s, calling itself 'The Unicorn'. If I remember rightly, Swart and a couple of his Jewish artist friends had grown obsessed with the idea of becoming Bohemian coffee-addicts and were just about to found a suitable establishment in Johannesburg, complete with its own magazine. They needed money for the project, of course, which they thought to get from Lady Oppenheimer, who wanted to convert a few of her husband's diamonds into real works of art. In any case, Lady Oppenheimer sent her Rolls Royce to pick up Swart and a dozen other Unicorns. I think it was Lippy Lipshitz who smashed one of the car's windows on getting in with a large wooden sculpture, which he had planned as a gift for their hostess. Despite that (or perhaps because of it), Lady Oppenheimer still fancied the idea of the magazine and coffee house and declared she was willing to donate 500 pounds, even though the Unicorns had not only broken the car window but also spilled red wine all over the carpet at dinner. Infused with enthusiasm, one of them (I believe it was Lipshitz again) wrote to Lady Oppenheimer that same evening, asking her to pose for him, whereupon he received a frosty refusal a few days later and none of the group quite dared to collect the promised funds. And that was the end of Johannesburg's artistic café culture.

Why am I writing this? Perhaps to illustrate to myself and to you, Mr Blatný (and possibly to you, Mr Martin) that a resemblance between two lives is an impossibility and that – even if such a thing were possible (and I stress: were!) – such a resemblance would not be based on similar prerequisites and indications. (How many people have ever stained Lady Oppenheimer's carpet with red wine? How many smashed the window of a Rolls Royce with a large wooden statue and proceeded to write smutty letters to the car's owner? And wherein, my dear Mr Blatný, are our lives supposed to resemble one another? (Mr Martin is free to answer this question, should he so wish.))

I don't want to put you off, Mr Blatný, but in the event of a correspondence we ought to start things out on a different footing. Tell me what life is like in Claybury and what brought you there. It is certainly not usual to write to a poet in an institution. Normally, both correspondents are in one.

Yours sincerely,
Nicholas Moore

Ivan Blatný to Nicholas Moore
(Blatný's reply to Nicholas Moore's first letter)

Claybury Hospital
Woodford Bridge

30th December 1962

Mr Martin has asked me to write to you again. I am now certain he is reading my letters.

It would be nice if we could talk about the weather. Usually there is not as much of it in England as in Brno, but now it's different, for it has been snowing for four days and all those who are English or feel like they are go out and measure the snow. The men here have made a sport out of it, and there is a competition between them. They have divided up the round houses on the lawn outside our block between them and measure the height of the snow on the roofs. William Milhodian has already fallen down and reduced the snow level beneath him to two inches. On the roofs, however, it is sixteen, and tomorrow it will be even more. Which house will win I do not know, as I do not have one and prefer weathers to wagers.

I am sorry about the poetry. But I am no longer a poet either. Not even in my own way. I am sitting here watching the men measuring snow, and my hand is growing cold and freezing off.

Ivan Blatný

Nicholas Moore to Ivan Blatný

89 Oakdene Road,
St Mary Cray, Kent

8th January 1963

Mr Blatný, you may not be a poet but it is certainly better to follow your words than to ruin one's eyes on the *TLS*. The front page of the 4th January edition is garnished with a drawing of the Radcliffe Camera, the library in Oxford financed by a tidy sum from the book-despiser John Radcliffe. So please don't be surprised by men in England climbing onto the roofs of round houses to measure the snow level. (Incidentally, the Rad Cam is also a round building, and if ever a literary critic should have the idea of measuring the snow at a height of 90 feet, I shall be all too happy to note down his findings on ground level.)

10th January

I had put this letter in its envelope and was just about to place it in the calloused hands of the Royal Mail, when I came across an article in the *TLS* last night – do forgive my rather monotonous-seeming reading behaviour – which left me quite perplexed, so much so that I am still sitting here. I am writing to you because I ~~believe~~ hope you can help me – and because I assume a reply from you would be a way of finding out a little of your story. (I have not yet had an opportunity to obtain any information about you. All I know is that you are apparently a Czech, you live in Claybury and – in contrast to myself – understand something of politics, at least enough to hold lectures on the subject.)

Mr Blatný, the thing that has shackled me to this seat bleached by the English sun is the following: as I read yesterday evening, the Soviet Communist Party held its 22nd congress fifteen months ago. This type of event does not usually interest me, and – if at all – I imagine it as a symmetrical arrangement of human bodies in concrete, grey and with artificial flowers. Be that as it may, when I read the aforementioned report I found out that two Russian writers – Alexander Tvardovsky and Nikolai Gribachov (whose names I had never heard before) – were elected as probationary members of the Central Committee of the Communist Party, while another author, also absolutely unknown to me, by the name of Mikhail Sholokhov, has obviously passed his probationary period and is now a full member of the Central Committee. Now, that alone would not be worth tearing open a sealed letter, but shortly below that I read that Mr Tvardovsky and Mr Gribachov spoke at the congress and that Mr Tvardovsky – according to the article's writer the editor of *Novy Mir* (New World?), the 'best and most courageous of Soviet literary magazines' – received 'stormy, prolonged applause' for his speech, while Mr Gribachov, who edits the magazine *Soviet Union*, which appears monthly in sixteen languages, got merely 'prolonged applause' – and that this distinction in applause can be decisive for their fates. (Whereby the distinction is probably not even in the applause itself, but merely in the words with the aid of which it penetrates out through the concrete so as to nest within minds, which – at least as I imagine it – will one day only have to nod approval for the death of these men, once another has nodded through the decision.)

There were two other speakers, a certain Vsevolod Kochetov, who is not only the editor of *Oktyabr*, but also one of the main opponents of a more liberal cultural policy and got no more than 'applause', and the aforementioned Mr Sholokhov, whom the reporter claims takes no particular side on the cultural battle and received 'lengthy, stormy applause'.

Mr Blatný, please do not misunderstand me, but might one (with a moderate measure of immoderateness) not say that 'applause' is two inches of snow, 'prolonged applause' is approximately eight, 'stormy, prolonged applause' twelve and 'lengthy, stormy applause' sixteen? Might one not say that, Mr Blatný?

Respectfully,
Nicholas Moore

I enclose a clipping of the publisher's advertisement for my first and, I hope, only horticultural book. It is about the tall bearded iris and was published, as you will see, ~~six~~ seven years ago. You may take it, apart from the poem cut out by whoever it was, as proof that I really exist and Mr Martin is not pulling your leg. And incidentally, should the said Mr Martin have any money at his disposal, do try and convince him to buy the book. In contrast to poetry, books about bearded irises have an expiry date – and I still have very many of them here. They might one day make the mountain of paper surrounding me collapse.

With thanks,
Nicholas Moore

PS: I'm afraid all the snow is not good for my flowers. Their lives have become shorter than those of my poems. They die before they make it onto paper.

Ivan Blatný to Nicholas Moore

16th March 1963

Mr Martin is saying nothing, and nor am I. But he doesn't know why I am doing it. And if he does, then only from reading my letters.

What else can I say?

It's true, I am a Czech, but my fate is England. I have built my nest in it like the blackbird behind Pustvik's grave in the Komárov churchyard. Here in Claybury, where we polish the corridors fourteen feet wide.

When it's too cold outside we sit in them in long rows, and I blow cigarette smoke into the air and watch it wafting through the sea to my feet. We always polish the floor ourselves, and when we do it well it looks like water. And like sky. And is still earth. English earth, Mr Moore, not Czech.

Mr Martin tells me to tell you I have nothing to tell you about the Russians.

I told him I have nothing to tell about the Russians, but he told me to write it down.

I have nothing to tell about the Russians, Mr Moore.

Nothing the Russians don't already know.

Ask me something about the French, about Céline, Simenon or Baudelaire. Baudelaire, whom a lady brought to Claybury many years ago.

We sat in a small room and the men were masturbating outside the window, and she gave me *Les Fleurs du Mal* and never came back.

Englishwomen have large bodies, Mr Moore, much larger than Czechwomen. But I like that. And if I ever get the chance to touch one I shall make use of it.

Mr Martin has just brought me a magazine and told me to send off the letter. He seems to have nothing to read. (But I didn't say that, of course.)

He hasn't told me anything about your book, Mr Moore, but let's make him wait a little longer.

Mr Moore, I never saw artificial flowers in Czechoslovakia. But I never went to Moscow either. I only know how the seeds rattled in the tin cans back home in Brno. There was a time when I could tell a flower by its sound.

Mr Martin has just been here again. He says we're getting mixed rooms, and my excitement is great. I shall send off the letter. While he reads it I shall pleasure myself with an Englishwoman.

There is only one more thing to say: the Russians, Mr Moore, do not believe in death. Neither in mine nor in their own. The Russians bring death. Just like the Germans brought Jiří his death, on his birthday, his twenty-second. All those bring death who have exchanged their jester's shoes for boots.

Rapping
onto cobblestones a good man's head.
Clapping
at a congress a man into his grave.

The snow has melted. Ivan Blatný: 1 inch.

Nicholas Moore to Ivan Blatný

89 Oakdene Road,
St Mary Cray, Kent

28th March 1963

Mr Blatný, I must admit to having not worn my jester's shoes when I disembarked from the train yesterday at precisely 10:32 am and my feet touched Oxford ground without hesitation. For a man who has spent the most years of his life in Cambridge, such an omission is tantamount to a crime, or at least a missed opportunity, yet in defence of my honour, I will say that I was not wearing boots either. I crept into Radcliffe's Camera in plain leather shoes, and should God have been so merciful as to let one or two critics fall from their day's work in the dizzying heights of literature, then they had already been cleared from the lawn by the time I arrived.

As usual, the interior of the Radder was filled with canonical swotting and book-learning; however, the book I had ordered was waiting for me, and once one of the parchment-coloured Oxford librarians had been so kind as to give it to me, I immediately descended into Acland's only saving tunnel, flicked my way north to the Bodleian and read the book on the way. That is, I didn't really read it, for the work in question is the second volume of an encyclopaedia by the name of *Slovník soudobých českých spisovatelů. Krásné písemnictví v letech 1918–45*, and I don't speak Czech.

However, your name is printed on p 967 – and after it the words 'lyrická poesie'.

Now, I don't venture to determine whether one and a half lines in an encyclopaedia make a man a poet, even though those two words allow few other interpretations. Be that as it may, those Bohemian words read beneath English earth clarified a number of matters for me. And the fact that you informed me you had stopped being a poet only confirms that you once were one.

I cannot and will not judge whether you still are one in the meantime, yet nor do I believe any other yardstick exists than one's own person. I fear I must thus correct myself slightly, or let us say explain myself better, for claiming I am now only a poet in my own way opens the floodgates to false modesty; it is, after all, the only way to lend expression to the poetic cause. For what other way than his own could a poet ever have? And in which other way could he express himself? In short, I shall strike out the 'now' and the 'only' – and would like to find out

why you have struck out the 'lyricka poesie' after
your name.

    With thanks,
    Nicholas Moore

Ivan Blatný to Nicholas Moore

19th April 1963

I have not seen Mr Martin for two weeks. They told me he had gone away for a while, but not where to, but I am certain he is staying in Oxford and combing the despicable library for traces of my past. I'd like to ask the nurses to find out more, but they have barricaded themselves into their five-doored house, and so I lend the kitchen ladies a hand and peel potatoes and find out all about their lives. And yet I fear everyone will be disappointed in the end. That is, everyone but me, for whatever Mr Martin brings back will sound Greek to his English ears. Whatever he digs up is only a fragment, a shard of a newer tragedy, the sign of the coming ostrakismos. Claybury, however, is my asylum. Here, they don't scratch my name on the ground, and if they do then I shall polish and polish the floor until the English earth swallows up the Czech word.

Ivan Blatný

Nicholas Moore to Ivan Blatný

26th April 1963

Mr Blatný, I turned Radcliffe's entire damned Camera on its head and then dragged myself half a mile between Oxford's monumental edifices in my raddled leather shoes to pay a visit to the Slavonic and – how fitting! – Modern Greek Collection at the Taylorian Library, and all I could find about you was one and a half lines in that unpronounceable Czech encyclopaedia, somewhere between two men by the names of Josef Biskup and Pavel Bojar, which is all I know about the two of them.

Just what is it we are supposed to have in common, Mr Blatný? And why, for goodness' sake, would anyone think we'd led similar lives?
(Should Mr Martin have turned up again, he can answer these questions. I suggest he sticks to the Greek, plays at Plutarch and writes his own *Parallel Lives*.)

Respectfully,
Nicholas Moore

PS: I found a photo of you in the appendix to the unpronounceable book. You look a little sad, it seems to me. Be that as it may, the index tells me that you and your work are actually listed on p 80; however, I fear that refers to the first volume, and that is not to be had here at all.

Ivan Blatný to Nicholas Moore

> 1st May 1963: Svátek práce
> International Workers' Day
> May Day / ~~Mayday~~

1919: born in Brno
1938: *Druhá hra na povídku* – with Jiří Orten
1938 (or 1939?): *Hra na povídku* – also with Jiří
1940: *Paní Jitřenka*
1941: *Melancholické procházky*
1945: *Tento večer*
1946: *Na kopané*
1947: *Hledání přítomného času*
1947: *Jedna, dvě, tři, čtyři, pět*

Nicholas Moore to Ivan Blatný

5th May 1963

Did you write that, Mr Blatný?

Ivan Blatný to Nicholas Moore

15th May 1963

Yes.

PS: Mr Martin has no Czech.

Nicholas Moore to Ivan Blatný

19th May 1963

1918: born in Cambridge
1938–1940: *Seven* – literary journal,
with J Goodland
1941 *A Wish in Season / The Island and the Cattle /
A Book for Priscilla / Buzzing Around with a Bee*
1942 *The Cabaret, the Dancer, the Gentlemen*
1944 *The Glass Tower / Thirty-Five Anonymous Odes*
1945 *The War of the Little Jersey Cows* – as 'Guy Kelly'
1945 *The Anonymous Elegies and other poems* –
anonymous
1950 *Recollections of the Gala. Selected Poems 1943–48*

That was me, Nicholas Moore.

PS: I suggest we end our round of introductions
herewith and officially go on saying nothing.

Nicholas Moore to Ivan Blatný

1st June 1963

I'm afraid I have expressed myself clumsily once again. What I wanted to say in my last letter was: write to me, Mr Blatný, write to me!

PS: I have started learning a little Czech. I have already managed to translate the title of one of your books. It is called 'One, two, three, four, five'. And this morning I thought of this:

> Five words make a sentence.
> Four words make four
> Three make three
> Two two
> One?
> One word makes the next.

Addendum

Ivan Blatný was transferred from Claybury to the 'House of Hope' in Ipswich on 4th June 1963. In 1977 he was moved to the 'Bixley Ward-Warren House' at St Clement's Hospital in Ipswich and in 1985 to Clacton-on-Sea. Ivan Blatný died in Colchester General Hospital on 5th August 1990.

There is no indication that Nicholas Moore ever received any more post from Ivan Blatný. He died on 26th January 1986 in a London hospital.

GLOSSARY

This list includes only those persons whose significance for Blatný or Moore is not obvious from the letters themselves.

Letter from Blatný to Moore, 10 December 1962
Blatný mentions in this letter a certain 'Doctor Martin'. He is referring here to the psychiatrist Dr Dennis Martin. Martin had started working at Claybury Hospital in 1955, introducing the concept of the 'therapeutic community', in which the psychiatrist abandons his traditionally paternalistic role as doctor and integrates the patients and the entire staff of a clinic directly into the therapy process. Blatný later named the poem 'Dr Martin's House' after him.

Letter from Moore to Blatný, 30 December 1962
Here, Nicholas Moore recalls a man by the name of Douglas Newton, who is in fact the poet, editor and later chairman of the Department of Primitive Art at the New York Metropolitan Museum, Bryan Leslie Douglas Newton (1920–2001). Newton and Moore co-edited the London literary journal *Seven* together during the 1940s.

Referred to by Moore several times in this letter as Lippy Lipshitz, Israel-Isaac Lipshitz (1903–1980) was one of the most significant South African sculptors. Lipshitz, who also worked with paint and prints, took part in the Venice Biennale in 1950, among other exhibitions. In 1978 he emigrated to Israel, where he died two years later.

The person referred to by Moore as 'Lady Oppenheimer' is the first wife of the diamond magnate Sir Ernest Oppenheimer. Of British origin, she was called Mary Lina Pollak until her marriage in 1906. She died in 1934.

Letter from Blatný to Moore, 16 March 1963
The 'Jiří' mentioned in Blatný's letter is the Czech poet Jiří Orten, who was a friend of Blatný's in his youth. On 30 August 1941, his 22nd birthday, he was run over by a German ambulance in Prague and severely injured. The General Hospital in occupied Prague refused to admit him, however. Orten, a Jew with the given name of Ohrenstein, was then taken to a different hospital but died of his injuries two days later.

In this letter, Blatný also refers to the grave of a certain Pustvik in the Komárov cemetery. There are over a dozen places by the name of Komárov in the modern-day Czech Republic and Slovakia. As Blatný originated from Brno, however, it is likely that the Komárov he mentions here is the district of that name in the city. There is no indication as yet, however, to whom the name Pustvik might refer.

Letter from Moore to Blatný, 26 April 1963
This letter mentions the Greek popular philosopher and biographer Plutarch of Chaeronea (ca. 45–125 AD), who wrote a series of biographies known as the *Parallel Lives*. In them, he compares a particular Greek military commander or statesman with his Roman equivalent.

Francis Nenik

Francis Nenik works as a farmer and writes in his free time. He has published several novels. Current works include *XO* (a novel in the form of a loose-leaf collection) as well as a collection of short stories with strict alliteration (2013). His most recent work, in which *The Marvel of Biographical Bookkeeping* appears, is the volume of stories *Francis Travels Backwards, or The Realignment of the 20th Century,* published by ed[ition]. cetera in Leipzig.